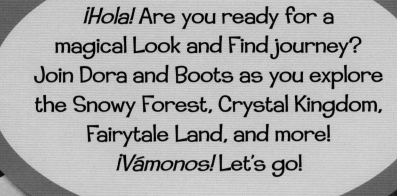

¡Hola! Are you ready for a magical Look and Find journey? Join Dora and Boots as you explore the Snowy Forest, Crystal Kingdom, Fairytale Land, and more! *¡Vámonos!* Let's go!

Published by Louis Weber, C.E.O., Publications International, Ltd.
7373 North Cicero Avenue, Lincolnwood, Illinois 60712
Ground Floor, 59 Gloucester Place, London W1U 8JJ

Customer Service: 1-800-595-8484 or customer_service@pilbooks.com

www.pilbooks.com

p i kids is a trademark of Publications International, Ltd., and is registered in the United States.
Look and Find is a trademark of Publications International, Ltd., and is registered in the United States and Canada.

8 7 6 5 4 3 2 1

Manufactured in USA.

ISBN-13: 978-1-4508-4207-5
ISBN-10: 1-4508-4207-0

We saved the Snow Princess from the witch and brought snow to the Snowy Forest! *¡Excelente!* Will you find all the snowy things that bring snow to the Snowy Forest?

We need to find everything that will help us bring color back to the Crystal Kingdom. Will you help?

We need to help Mariana clean up Mermaid Kingdom. Will you help us find all the garbage that shouldn't be here?

We made it to Fairytale Land! We need to save Sleeping Boots! ¡Vámonos!

We're on Star Mountain to get back my necklace. *¡Mira las estrellas!* Let's look for Explorer Stars to help us climb to the top!

Will you help me find what I need for my ballet recital?

We made it to the Enchanted Forest. We need to find all of our Enchanted Forest friends!

When I Grow Up

Illustrated by A & J Studios

Mi mami is an archaeologist. She digs for treasure and explores to learn about how people lived a long time ago. When I grow up, I might want to be an archaeologist, too. Will you help me find these things?

Mi primo Diego is an animal rescuer. He helps animals in trouble. Boots and I are helping him check up on the rainforest animals today. Do you see these animals?

Dora and Boots to the rescue! Boots and I could be firefighters like Tico's *mami*. We're helping this kitten get out of the tree. Will you help find these firefighter things?

Goal! *Mi amigo* Tico wants to be a soccer star. Help us find these different soccer balls.

Isa wants to be an astronaut and explore outer space in her rocket ship. Will you help her find these things in space?

Giddy-up! My friend Benny wants to be a cowboy. Boots and I are helping him practice here on the ranch. Do you see these cowboy things?

Scavenger Hunt

Illustrated by Bob Roper

¡*Hola!* I'm Dora. Today in school, my teacher Maestra Beatriz gave us a homework project. It's a scavenger hunt! The scavenger hunt starts here in my classroom. I need to find something that starts with each letter of the alphabet. Will you help me?

Boots is going to help us with the scavenger hunt, too! Let's find these things on the playground.

one slide
un resbalón

two seesaws
dos balancines

four bicycles
cuatro bicicletas

three swings
tres columpios

five sand castles
cinco castillos de arena

seven bats
siete bates

eight baseballs
ocho beisbols

six mitts
seis guantes de beisbol

nine soccer balls
nueve fútbols

ten marbles
diez canicas

Where can we find the rest of the things on the scavenger hunt list? Let's ask Map! Help us match the places we need to go with the pictures on Map.

Benny's Farm

Nutty Forest

Isa's Flowery Garden

Mucky Mud

Shape Forest

Next on our scavenger hunt list are shapes. We can look for them in Shape Forest! Will you help us find these shapes?

rectangle
el rectángulo

oval
el óvalo

circle
el círculo

square
el cuadrado

diamond
el losange

triangle
el triángulo

Now we need to find things that go! Tico always has lots of those. Will you come with us to look for these things at Tico's Workshop in the Nutty Forest?

car
el coche

airplane
el avión

motorcycle
la motocicleta

wagon
la carreta

balloon
el globo

rowboat
el bote

We want to go to Isa's Flowery Garden, but first we need to cross the Mucky Mud! Can you find these items that will help us get across?

stilts
los zancos

rope
la cuerda

springs
los muelles

hang glider
el ala delta

vine
la enredadera

ladder
la escalera

We've made it to Isa's Flowery Garden! Next on the scavenger hunt list are colors. Let's find a flower for each color.

orange
anaranjada

yellow
amarilla

red
roja

purple
morada

blue
azul

pink
rosada

white
blanca

We're almost done with the scavenger hunt. I just need to find these farm animals. Will you help me look for them at Benny's Farm?

pig
el cerdo

cow
la vaca

duck
el pato

goat
la cabra

sheep
el carnero

chicken
el pollo

horse
el caballo

Animal Rescue Adventure

Illustrated by A & J Studios

¡Hola! I'm Diego, and this is my sister, Alicia! We're Animal Rescuers. We rescue animals and take care of them here at the Animal Rescue Center. Do you see the gear we use on our rescue missions?

Rescue Pack

video watch

field journal

sticky gloves

Click

spotting scope

My whole family works at the Animal Rescue Center. We rescue lots of animals in the rainforest. See if you can find my family and my rainforest animal friends.

Papi

Baby Jaguar

spectacled bear

Alicia

Mami

Bobo Brothers

Sammy the Sloth

Animal Rescuers like me don't just rescue rainforest animals. I travel to many locations to help animals. I've helped lots of animals here at the beach. Will you find the animal friends I've helped that live on the sand or in the ocean?

blue shark

seagull

leatherback sea turtle

jellyfish

harbor seal

humpback whale

Now let's go back to the rainforest, where lots of different animals live. Look for these baby rainforest animals and their mommies.

pygmy marmosets

howler monkeys

jaguars

spider monkeys

sloths

maned wolves

We also help animals who live high in the mountains. The air is thin and cold up here, but there are still lots of animals. Will you find these mountain animals?

Mami Jaguar

chinchilla

Linda the Llama

condor

mountain tapir

puma

We also help animals all the way down in Antarctica, at the very bottom of the world! Brrr! It's really, really cold, but there are still lots of animals that live here. Try to find these Antarctic animals ... and those silly Bobo Brothers!

Adélie penguin

Bobo Brothers

orca

chinstrap penguin

sperm whale

emperor penguin

This is the desert. There's sand everywhere and it can get really, really hot during the day. But even though this is a hot and sandy place, many animals call the desert their home.

prairie dog

roadrunner

coyote

tarantula

bat

rattlesnake

We made it back to the Animal Rescue Center. Click the Camera took a lot of pictures of the great places we went and all of the animals we saw - including a whole lot of baby animals! Will you look in the pictures here to spot these different baby animals?

baby
spectacled bear

baby puma

baby coyote

baby orca

baby caiman

baby leatherback
sea turtle

Go back through the entire book to complete these challenges!

Can you find these magical things?

- snowman
- flying fairy
- Mariana the Mermaid
- magical music box
- rainbow
- unicorn
- crowned star

Do you see Boots doing these things?

- flying
- sleeping
- helping
- playing
- riding
- listening

Find and count these things in Dora and Diego's adventures.

- 1 camera
- 2 rowboats
- 3 wheelbarrows
- 4 snakes
- 5 whales
- 6 hot-air balloons
- 7 hats
- 8 seashells
- 9 penguins
- 10 turtles

Baby Jaguar is one of Diego's best friends. How many times do you see Baby Jaguar in this book?